Brindle Bear
Telling the Time

By John Patience

Printed in Hungary for the publishers
Peter Haddock Ltd. U.K.

One morning, as he was eating his breakfast, Brindle Bear received a telephone call from his Uncle Grimble. "I would like to come to visit you this evening," said Grimble. "Could you pick me up at the railway station at 6 o'clock?" "Certainly," replied Brindle. "Cheerio." Then Brindle began to wonder how he would know when it was 6 o'clock. "I know," he said to himself. "I'll buy a wrist watch."

So the clever bear drove into the town to see his good friend Lionel, the clock and watchmaker. It was **9 o'clock** and Lionel had just opened his shop.

There were so many clocks and watches in Lionel's shop that it took Brindle half an hour to choose the one he liked best. The time was now **half past nine**.

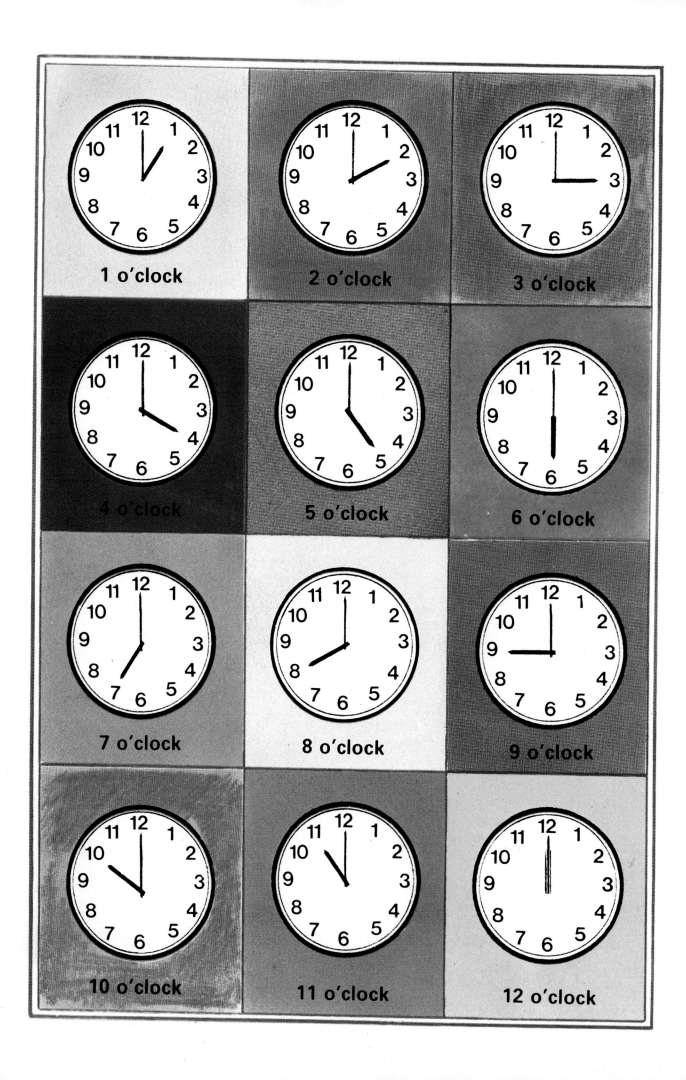

"Now I will teach you how to tell the time, so that you can use your watch properly," said Lionel. "This picture shows what the face of your watch will look like at different times of day."

"We can divide each hour up into quarters. There are sixty minutes in every hour, so a quarter of an hour is fifteen minutes."

"This is a quarter past one."

"This is half past one."

"This is a quarter to two."

When Lionel had finished teaching Brindle how to tell the time, the excited little bear rushed off to show his new watch to his friend Amber, the tiger. The time was now **10 o'clock**.

It was **11 o'clock** when Brindle arrived at Amber's house. Amber was very impressed by Brindle's watch. "It's a lovely watch," she said. "And I see it's **11 o'clock**, time for a cup of tea. Would you like one?" "Yes please," said Brindle.

At **a quarter past eleven** Brindle helped Amber to water her garden.

At **a quarter to twelve** he helped her to pick apples in
the orchard.

After picking the apples Brindle said "Goodbye," to Amber and set off in his car to show his new watch to his friend Rollo. But by **12 o'clock (mid-day)** the sun was so hot that the radiator in Brindle's car boiled dry! Fortunately Farmer Bill was passing by. "Never mind," he said. "Just wait here and I'll fetch some water from the farm."

In ten minutes, at **ten past twelve**, Farmer Bill came back with a jug of cold water and filled Brindle's radiator.

In another five minutes, at **a quarter past twelve**, Brindle was on his way again.

It was **1 o'clock** when Brindle reached Rollo's cottage. Rollo was as impressed as Amber had been by Brindle's new watch and, as it was lunch time, he invited his friend to share a beautiful blackberry pie with him.

After they had eaten the pie and washed the dishes, the time was **half past two**. "Let's go fishing," suggested Rollo. "That's a splendid idea," said Brindle. "Perhaps we shall catch some trout for tea."

The walk to their favourite fishing spot was quite a long one and it took the two friends half an hour, so the time was now **3 o'clock**.

They fished for two whole hours, until **5 o'clock**, and neither of them caught a thing. Then, as Rollo was casting his line, he got it tangled around the neck of a swan. The poor bird was very angry and chased Brindle and Rollo away.

"Well, no fish for tea tonight," sighed Brindle. "Never mind," replied Rollo. "I've got lots of lovely sausages in the larder." By **6 o'clock** Rollo had cooked the sausages and Brindle was setting the table. After tea the two contented animals sat by the fireside and chatted, until at last Brindle decided he had better go home.

The time had passed quickly, and it was now **8 o'clock**, and as Brindle drove home the moon and stars were shining brightly in the night sky.

It was **9 o'clock** when Brindle arrived home and what a surprise he got. There on his doorstep sat Uncle Grimble. "Oh no!" exclaimed Brindle. "I forgot to pick you up at the station." "You certainly did," replied Uncle Grimble. "And I had to walk all the way here carrying this grandfather clock. It's a present for you!"

Here are some telling-the-time questions.
Brindle has stopped work for a tea break. What time is it?

Brindle has been invited to a party. He should be there by 2 o'clock. What time is it now?
Is he late?

Brindle and Amber have found something rather strange — a Windmill Clock! What time does it say?

What time does Brindle go to bed?